W9-BZQ-982

The Music Hour

First Book

by

Osbourne McConathy

Formerly Director of the Department of Public School Music, Northwestern University

W. Otto Miessner

Formerly Director of the School of Music, State Teachers College, Milwaukee, Wisconsin

Edward Bailey Birge

Professor of Public School Music, Indiana University

Mabel E. Bray

Director of Music, New Jersey State Teachers College,
Trenton, New Jersey

Illustrated by

Shirley Kite

Silver, Burdett and Company

New York   Newark   Boston   Chicago   San Francisco

ACKNOWLEDGMENTS

The courtesy of the following authors and publishers in allowing the use of copyrighted material is gratefully acknowledged:

Doubleday, Doran and Company for "Animal Crackers" by Christopher Morley from *Songs for a Little House* (copyright, 1917).

Henry Holt and Company for "I Had a Little Doggy" from *The Home Book of Verse for Young Folks*, selected and arranged by Burton Egbert Stevenson.

Lothrop, Lee & Shepard Company for "The Lovable Child" from *Child Stories and Rhymes* by Emilie Poulsson.

New England Publishing Company for the use of "Thanksgiving" by R. N. Turner from *American Primary Teacher*.

F. A. Owen for the use of "A Cure for Crossness" by Harriet G. Brown from *Primary Plans*.

Alice B. Parisien for the melody, "Following the Winds."

Rand, McNally & Company for the use of Wilhelmina Seegmiller's poem, "Where We Get Our Bread" from *Little Rhymes for Little Readers*.

Charles Scribner's Sons for "Toyland" by Eugene Field.

Katherine Tynan Hinkson for "Chanticleer."

Grateful acknowledgment is also due Dr. Emma Grant Meader, formerly instructor in Elementary Education, Teachers College, Columbia University, for her selection and supervision of the choice of poetry; Mrs. Florence E. Dangerfield, Director of the Department of Physical Education, Bradford Academy, for her assistance in correlating rhythmic activities with the vocal music lesson; Mrs. Shirley Kite Smith for her illustrations; Mrs. Howard Van Sinderen and Professor Daniel Gregory Mason for the permission to reproduce the photograph and autograph of Mr. Lowell Mason; and all the poets and composers whose contributions have won the heart of youth and captured its imagination.

Special recognition is due for the poems in this book written by the late Abbie Farwell Brown. Up to the end she worked unstintedly and self-forgetfully that the children who sing from this book may unlock a new gate in the land of fact and fancy for which her verses forever hold a key.

Piano accompaniments are provided in the Elementary Teacher's Book to accompany the First and Second Books.

COPYRIGHT, 1927, 1928, BY

SILVER, BURDETT AND COMPANY

PRINTED IN THE UNITED STATES OF AMERICA

DEAR CHILDREN,

This is your song and picture book. You will like the songs because the melodies are beautiful, and the stories tell about many things which you enjoy every day.

There are songs that many children before you have loved to sing; and others that were written for you.

You will also like the pictures for they tell you what the music says.

Singing makes people happy. It is good to sing, because it helps you to show how happy you are. Singing together is great pleasure for all of us.

Of course you have already learned a number of songs. With the words and notes before you, it will now be possible for you to help in the Music Hour. Soon you will be able to learn your own songs from the notes.

Singing is fun. We want you to have fun singing the songs in this book. We know you will be glad that we made it for you.

Osbourne McConathy

W. Otto Messner

Edward B. Birge

Mabel E. Bray

Lowell Mason

To Lowell Mason, the Father of Public School Music in America, who introduced music into the schools of Boston in 1837, this FIRST BOOK of THE MUSIC HOUR is gratefully dedicated.

The Music Hour

FIRST BOOK

Open the Windows

Rote Song

ABBIE FARWELL BROWN

LOWELL MASON

O - pen, lit - tle eye - lids,
All the lit - tle win - dows,

Night has flown a - way,
Cur - tained for the night,

Through your hap - py win - dows
Wide a - wake and smil - ing,

Greet the glad new day.
O - pen to the light.

Good Morning!

Rote Song

G. A. GRANT-SCHAEFER   G. A. GRANT-SCHAEFER

Good morn - ing! Good morn - ing!

Good morn - ing!

The sun shines a - bove us to - day;

So we'll work while we work,

And play while we play.

That's the way to be hap - py and gay.

Jack and Jill

Rote Song

MOTHER GOOSE

FAY FOSTER

With humor

Jack and Jill went up the hill

To fetch a pail of wa - ter;

Jack fell down and broke his crown

And Jill came tum - bling af - ter.

A Cure for Crossness
Rote Song

HARRIET G. BROWN   HORATIO PARKER

I   felt   so ver - y   cross   one   time

I   did - n't   know   what   to   say,

But   I   made   a   lit - tle   smile   come

And   the   cross - ness   ran____ a - way.

In the Orchard

Rote Song

Julia Colton Willard

W. Otto Miessner

One, two, three, dance with me,

Gai - ly skip - ping, trip - ping 'neath the ap - ple tree!

How we fly, you and I,

Hap - py, mer - ry chil - dren we.

I Had a Little Doggy

Rote Song

NURSERY RHYME

ANICE TERHUNE

Gently

I had a lit - tle dog - gy

That used to sit and beg;

But dog - gy tum - bled down the stairs

And broke his lit - tle leg.

Oh! Dog-gy I will nurse you,

To try and make you well,

And you shall have a col-lar, too,

And lit-tle sil-ver bell.

Feathers

Observation Song

JEAN NEAL   ELEANOR SMITH

Feath - ers   in   a   pi - geon's breast!
You   and   I   could   nev - er   grow

Who   has   ev - er   seen
An - y - thing   so   fine.

Bright - er   blue   or   am - e - thyst,
On - ly   lit - tle   pi - geons know

Chang - ing   red   and   green?
How   they   glow   and   shine.

The Children That People Love

Reading Song

EMILIE POULSSON

Adapted

Frisk - y   as   a   lamb,
Hap - py   as   a   lark,

Bus - y   as   a   bee,
Gen - tle   as   a   dove,

That's   the   kind   of   boy
That's   the   kind   of   girl

Peo - ple   like   to   see.
Ev - 'ry   one   will   love,

Ride a Cock Horse

Rote Song

MOTHER GOOSE

J. W. ELLIOTT

Ride a cock horse to Ban - bu - ry Cross,

To see a fine la - dy up - on a white horse;

Rings on her fin - gers and bells on her toes,

She shall have mu - sic wher - ev - er she goes.

The Dancers
Rote Song

NATHAN HASKELL DOLE

GERMAN FOLK TUNE

As the tu-lips are toss-ing their del-i-cate heads
So we greet one an-oth-er with bow and gay glance

Dressed in their yel-lows and pur-ples and reds,
When we ar-rive at the end of the dance.

Gratitude

Observation Song

ABBIE FARWELL BROWN   GEORGE L. WRIGHT

White   or   brown   or   spot - ted   cow,
If   I   came   to   call   on   you,

Liv - ing   some - where   far   a - way,
My   po - lit - est   thanks   to   say,

I   should   like   to   thank   you   now
You   would   toss   your   head   and   moo;

For   the   milk   I   drink   each   day.
I   should   bow,   and   say   "Good   day!"

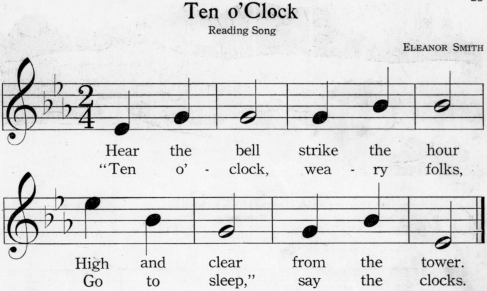

Ten o'Clock

Reading Song

ELEANOR SMITH

Hear the bell strike the hour
"Ten o' - clock, wea - ry folks,

High and clear from the tower.
Go to sleep," say the clocks.

The Candy Man

Reading Song

ANN UNDERHILL

ELEANOR SMITH

Come and buy my sticks of can - dy!
Have your dimes and pen - nies han - dy;

Chil - dren, chil - dren, step this way!
See my ver - y fine dis - play.

The Street Car

Rote Song

Minnie E. Hicks

G. A. Grant-Schaefer

I love to watch the street cars

That run a - long so fast,

And peo - ple at the win - dows smile

At me as they go past.

14

So man - y, man - y peo - ple

Get on and off each car;

I won - der where they're go - ing,

I won - der who they are.

Hallowe'en

Study Song

Abbie Farwell Brown

W. Otto Miessner

Hal - low - e'en!   Hal - low - e'en!
Hal - low - e'en!   Hal - low - e'en!

Oh what fun - ny things are seen!
Lan - terns light the mag - ic scene.

Witch - es' hats, Coal black cats,
Danc - es queer, Shrieks of fear,

Broom - stick rid - ers, mice and rats!
Strang - est night in all the year!

Wild Geese

Rote Song

MAY MORGAN

CANADIAN FOLK SONG

Hear a cry, clear and high

Drift - ing down from the au - tumn sky,

Chil - dren all hear the call

Wild geese sound - ing a shrill "Good - by."

Skipping Song
Rote Song

NANCY BYRD TURNER   FRENCH MELODY

A - way we skip, a - way!

It's fun to be off, so mer - ri - ly go - ing,

It's fun to skip to - day,

In time with the tune, on twink - ling toe!

Thanksgiving

Rote Song

R. N. TURNER

EDWARD BAILEY BIRGE

Joy is in the par - lor, Fun is on the stair,
Oh, 'tis glad Thanksgiv-ing, Joy of all the year,

Bus-tle in the kitch-en, O-dors in the air!
Noth-ing half so hap-py, Noth-ing half so dear!

Laugh-ter in each dim-ple, Smile in ev-'ry eye!
Song and sport and pleas-ure Make the mo-ments fly,

Hap-py lit-tle maid-en, Can you tell me why?
Hap-py hearts and thankful; That's the rea-son why.

The Fisherman

Observation Song

ABBIE FARWELL BROWN

OLD MELODY

The   fish - er - man   gets   up   at   three,
He   fills   the   boat   with   sil - ver   things

When   ev - 'ry - one   is   sound   a - sleep,
That   glis - ten   in   the   ear - ly   light,

And   goes   out   on   the   cold   blue   sea
And   back   to   hun - gry   folk   he   brings

To   catch   the   fish - es   in   the   deep.
The   pre - cious   car - go   gleam - ing   bright.

The Traffic Cop

Reading Song

Ann Underhill

German Folk Song

He stands there in the mid-dle of the street!

The mo-tor cars go buzz! buzz! buzz!

The mo-tor horns go honk! honk! honk!

The mo-tor wheels go whiz-zing by his feet.

Armistice Day

Rote Song

NATHAN HASKELL DOLE

ITALIAN MELODY

All the bells ring the end of war,

It was peace the troops were fight - ing for!

So we march a - long, With a joy - ful song.

War shall cease, Hail to peace!

Soldiers' March
(Theme from record for marching)

ROBERT SCHUMANN

Gay Leaves Flying

Reading Song

Nina B. Hartford

Nina B. Hartford

Gay leaves fly - ing through the air,
But the snow - flakes soft and white,

Make the trees look cold and bare.
Soon will robe them all in white.

Squirrel Dear

Reading Song

Nina B. Hartford

Nina B. Hartford

Squir - rel dear, do not fear,
Take a few, come now do,

See I have some a - corns here.
I have brought them all for you.

On Christmas Eve

Rote Song

VIRGINIA BAKER

HORATIO PARKER

Ev - 'ry year on Christ - mas eve

Twink - ling stars see San - ta's sleigh,

High a - bove the chim - ney tops,

Drawn by pranc - ing rein - deer gay.

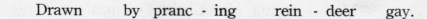

Sing a Song of Workshops

Rote Song

FREDERICK MANLEY

G. W. CHADWICK

Allegro

1. Sing a song of work-shops!
2. Plough-men in the mead-ows,
3. Tai-lors on their bench-es;
4. Sing a song of work-shops!

Bus - y men and things;
Fur - row - ing the soil,
Stu - dents in their rooms;
Bus - y men and boys;—

Black-smiths at the for - ges
Na - ture and her show - ers
Chil - dren at their les - sons;
San - ta in the North - land

Where the an - vil rings.
Bless - ing all their toil.
Weav - ers at their looms.
Mak - ing Christ - mas toys.

Jacky Frost

Rote Song

LAURA E. RICHARDS
By permission of Little, Brown & Co.

ELEANOR SMITH

Allegretto

Jack - y Frost, Jack - y Frost Came in the night,
Jack - y Frost, Jack - y Frost Crept round the house

Left the mead - ows that he cross'd All gleam - ing white;
Sly___ as a sil - ver fox, Still as a mouse.

Paint - ed with his sil - ver brush Ev - 'ry win - dow pane;
Out our lit - tle Jen - ny came, Blush-ing like a rose,

Kiss'd the leaves and made them blush, Blush and blush a - gain.
Up___ jump'd Jack-y Frost, And pinch'd her lit - tle nose.

Lullaby

Rote Song

MABEL E. BRAY

RUSSIAN FOLK SONG

Hush - a - by, my lit - tle dear - ie,

Bye, bye, lull - a - by;

Moth - er watch - es al - ways near thee,

Bye, bye, lull - a - by;

Fa - ther soon will come to cheer thee,

Bye, bye, lull - a - by.

Christmas Stockings

Rote Song

Agnes Choate Wonson

W. Otto Miessner

Three lit - tle stock-ings Hung in a row;

Three lit - tle chil - dren Watch - ing be - low,

It's Christ - mas Eve! It's Christ - mas Eve!

And they'll not leave till San - ta comes, I know!

Christmas Bells

Study Song

ELEANOR SMITH

Hark! I hear the bells are ring - ing

Mer - ry Christ - mas to us bring - ing.

Bim, bom, bim, bom, bim, bom, bell!

pp

Bim, bom, bell!

The Bells of Chazy

Bells in the Steeple

Reading Song

ELEANOR SMITH

Bells that hang high in the stee - ple,

Call - ing, "Come to church, good peo - ple";

Loud - ly ring and sing your song,

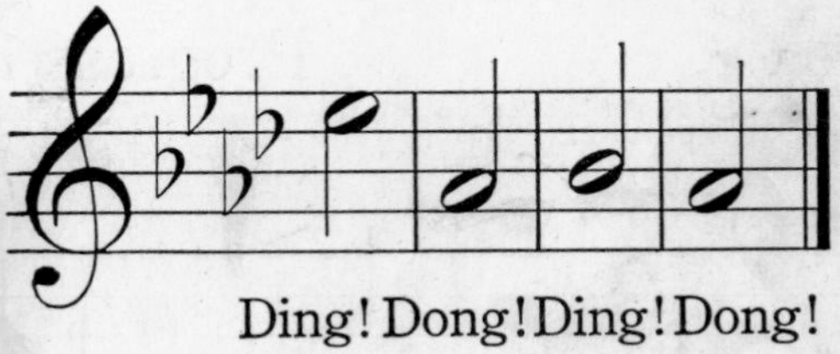

Ding! Dong! Ding! Dong!

Westminster Chimes

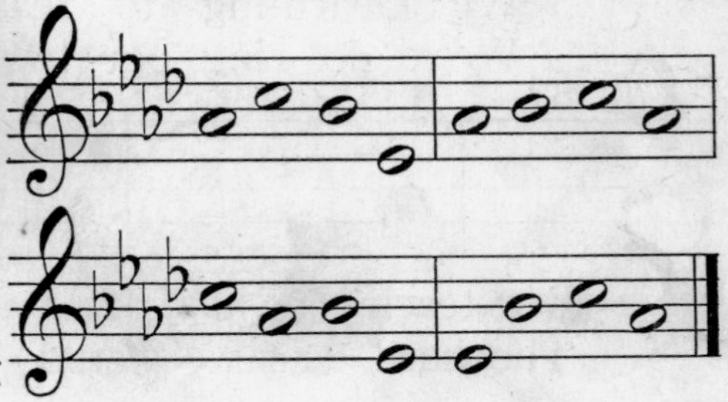

New Year
Observation Song

ABBIE FARWELL BROWN

EMMY KÖHLER

Let the horns and whis - tles blow,

So that all the world may know

One more hap - py year has come to bless our home!

Progress in School
Study Song

ANN UNDERHILL

ADAPTED

We're learn - ing to read and to write and to spell,
We're do - ing our best and as old - er we grow

The teach - er has told us we do ver - y well.
The hard - er we stud - y the more we shall know.

The Rag Man

Observation Song

ANN UNDERHILL   OLD MELODY

Old rags   and bot‑tles! Old rags   and   bot‑tles!

I'll   pay   well   for   your   rags!   Rags!

The Apple Man

Reading Song

ABBIE FARWELL BROWN   ADAPTED

Come buy my jui‑cy fruit, Fra‑grant and red!

Come and buy a ten cent ap‑ple, Big as your head.

The Sandman

Rote Song

Nina B. Hartford

Nina B. Hartford

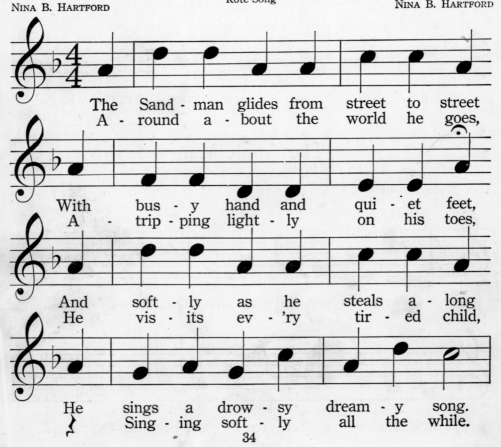

The Sand - man glides from street to street
A - round a - bout the world he goes,

With bus - y hand and qui - et feet,
A - trip - ping light - ly on his toes,

And soft - ly as he steals a - long
He vis - its ev - 'ry tir - ed child,

He sings a drow - sy dream - y song.
Sing - ing soft - ly all the while.

34

Sleep-y-time is here at last,

Work and play-ing all are past,

So sleep,__ sleep,__ sleep.__

Grandma

Observation Song

ANN UNDERHILL

OLD TUNE

When Grand - ma comes to vis - it,
She tells us of her school - mates,

Oh, then we are so hap - py,
Her fa - ther and her moth - er,

So glad to have her come;
And how they have used to live,

For, sit - ting by the win - dow
She tells us of her broth - ers,

She tells us fun - ny sto - ries
Her sis - ters and the oth - ers,

Of when she was a lit - tle girl.
And of the games they used to play.

The Balloon Man
Reading Song

ABBIE FARWELL BROWN

ADAPTED

When I am grown up I'll whis - tle some tunes,
To hold such a bunch would real - ly be fun;

And stand on the cor - ner and sell my bal - loons.
But I am so lit - tle I on - ly have one.

When Children Say "Good Morning"

Rote Song

PAULINE FRANCES CAMP

HARRIET WARE

When chil-dren say "Good Morn-ing,"

As prop-er chil-dren should,

I won-der if they ev-er think

What makes the morn-ing good?

'Tis not the mer - ry sun - beams,

Nor twit - ter of the birds;

But pleas - ant thoughts and hap - py smiles,

And gen - tle lov - ing words.

Lincoln

Study Song

ANN UNDERHILL

ELEANOR SMITH

Once there lived a splen - did man;
Firm but gen - tle; strong but kind;

Guess his name now if you can.
With his coun - try's good in mind;

Tall and thin, with care - worn face,
Pres - i - dent he came to be;

Great - est lead - er of his race.
Chil - dren, tell me! Who was he?

Animal Crackers

Rote Song

CHRISTOPHER MORLEY · · · MARSHALL BARTHOLOMEW

An - i - mal crack - ers and co - coa to drink,
What do you choose when you're off - ered a treat?

7 That is the fin - est of sup - pers, I think;
When Moth - er says, "What would you like most to eat?

7 When I'm grown up and can have what I please,
Is it waf - fles and syr - up, or cin - na - mon toast?"

I think I shall al - ways in - sist up - on these.
It's co - coa and an - i - mals that I love the most!

Following the Winds

Rote Song

NANCY BYRD TURNER

ALICE B. PARISIEN

Eastward, eastward, let us go, while the sky is all a-glow;

West-ward, west-ward, let us roam, far a-way from home!

Northward, northward, winds are bold, skies are bright and air is cold;

Southward, southward toward the sun; now our jour-ney's done!

42

Run and Hop

Rote Song

NANCY BYRD TURNER   SWEDISH FOLK TUNE

Run, run, run, and⎯ hop, hop, hop,

We'll sing and dance and nev - er stop;

Run, run, run, with laugh and song

We'll dance the whole day long.

Puss in the Corner

ANN UNDERHILL
Observation Song
POLISH FOLK SONG

Puss-y in the cor - ner, Come out from your cor - ner,
Puss-y in the cor - ner, Come out from your cor - ner,

Can you run the fast - er   Slip-ping quick-ly past her?
Ma - ry there can match you;   She will try to   catch you.

Jump in - to her cor - ner!   Jump in - to her cor - ner!
Ah! You need not scorn her!   Now she has your cor - ner!

Valentine's Day

ABBIE FARWELL BROWN
Study Song
ADAPTED

Not   a   cop - per   cent   is   mine,
Rob - in   chirp - ing   in   the   tree,

Who   will   be   my   Val - en - tine?
Make   a   val - en - tine   for   me.

Flag Song

Rote Song

MABEL E. BRAY

ROBERT SCHUMANN

Dear flag of our A - mer - i - ca,

How proud we are of you!

It makes us brave to see you wave

In folds red, white, and blue.

47

School Song

Study Song

ANN UNDERHILL

NELLIE POORMAN

Now the clock is strik - ing eight,
See the school doors o - pen wide;
Hark, the clock is strik - ing nine;

Ding dong! Ding dong!
Ding dong! Ding dong!
Ding dong! Ding dong!

Hur - ry or you will be late!
Now the chil - dren step in - side,
See the chil - dren's fac - es shine!

Ding ding dong!
Ding ding dong!
Sing a song!

The Snowbirds

Study Song

B. J. Reismann

Man - y dear snow-birds come troop-ing a - long,

Mak - ing the air full of twit - ter - ing song.

They flut - ter and twin - kle a - bout in the trees,

And let us come tow'rd them as near as we please.

1.

2.

Indian Echo Song

Rote Song

NANCY BYRD TURNER *   CHIPPEWA INDIAN CALL

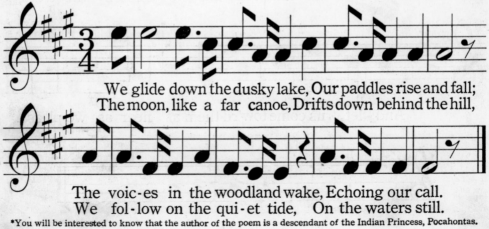

We glide down the dusky lake, Our paddles rise and fall;
The moon, like a far canoe, Drifts down behind the hill,

The voic-es in the woodland wake, Echoing our call.
We fol-low on the qui-et tide, On the waters still.

*You will be interested to know that the author of the poem is a descendant of the Indian Princess, Pocahontas.

50

Papoose

Rote Song

MABEL E. BRAY   NAVAJO INDIAN MELODY

Hush - a - by, hush - a - by, pa - poose, pa - poose,

Hush - a - by, ___ hush - a - by, ___ hush - a - by.

Where We Get Our Bread

Rote Song

WILHELMINA SEEGMILLER

W. OTTO MIESSNER

Coming Rain

Reading Song

ELEANOR SMITH

Sun's a - way, Skies are gray,

Rain will sure - ly come to - day.

Playing Horse

Reading Song

ELEANOR SMITH

Up the hill we're run-ning, Now we scam-per down,

We're the fast-est po - nies In this whole big town.

Marching Star

Rote Song

ABBIE FARWELL BROWN

LOWELL MASON

All the night, when I am sleep - ing,
In a great pro - ces - sion march - ing,

While the si - lent hours go by,
They are go - ing on their way,

Lit - tle stars their watch are keep - ing
By a path - way o - ver - arch - ing

Far a - bove me__ in the sky.
From the night in - to the day.

The New Moon
Study Song

VIRGINIA BAKER

G. A. GRANT-SCHAEFER

Shin - ing on high, up in the sky,

Like a bright air - ship the New Moon sails by.

A Sleigh Ride

Reading Song

From *St. Nicholas,*
by permission of the Century Company

ELEANOR SMITH

Jin - gle, jin - gle, off they go,

Stop! my hors - es, Whoa! then! Whoa!

Fruit
Reading Song

CHRISTINA ROSSETTI

I. T. WILSON

Cur -rants on a bush, Figs up - on a stem,

Cher -ries on a bending bough, And Ned to gath - er them.

Jump Rope

Observation Song

ABBIE FARWELL BROWN

MABEL E. BRAY

Jump the rope! Jump the rope!
Jump the rope! Jump the rope!

Hold it tight - ly, Skip - ping light - ly,
First I fum - bled; Then I stum - bled;

Swing it high! Swing it high!
Start once more! Start once more!

Two to - geth - er, you and I.
One and two and three and four.

Point Lightly, Partner

Rote Song

NANCY BYRD TURNER

GERMAN FOLK SONG

Point light - ly, part - ner, point and gai - ly slide;

Danc - ing is such fun, danc - ing by my side.

Now it's time to whirl you, next it's time to twirl you;

Point light - ly, part - ner, point and gai - ly slide!

A Million Little Sunbeams

Rote Song

The Youth's Companion   HORATIO PARKER

A   mil - lion   lit - tle   sun - beams

Can   make   a   pleas - ant   day,

A   mil - lion   lit - tle   rain - drops

Can   fright - en   them   a - way.

Winds of Evening
Study Song

ANN UNDERHILL

FRENCH MELODY

Winds of eve - ning whis - per - ing soft - ly,

Sweep like shad - ows o - ver the earth.

O - ver the earth and un - der the sky,

Winds of eve - ning whis - per - ing soft - ly

Sweep like shad - ows o - ver the earth.

Slumber Song

Rote Song

MABEL E. BRAY   JOHANN SEBASTIAN BACH

Hush - a - by, my   lit - tle ba - by,
Morn - ing sun - shine   will a - wake you,

Sleep un - til the   morn - ing light;
Fresh and bright, a   glad new day.

May God's an - gels   watch your sleep - ing
In the morn - ing   you will wak - en,

All the long and   qui et night
Glad to greet an - oth - er day

THE MADONNA OF THE CHAIR

In this famous picture the great Italian artist, Raphael, has painted a beautiful story of the love and devotion of the Madonna, the Christ Child, and the Child St. John.

The Firemen

Study Song

ANN UNDERHILL

ELEANOR SMITH

Clat-ter! Clat-ter! What's the matter? Fire! Fire! Fire!
Flames are roaring! Smoke is pouring! Higher! Higher! Higher!

Ring dong! Ding dong! Hear the big gong, Fire! Fire! Fire!
Brave men dar - ing! Peo-ple star-ing! Fire! Fire! Fire!

Now the en-gine's past, Rush-ing on so fast,
Hear the watch-ers shout, See they've put it out!

Feet are fly - ing, voic-es cry-ing Fire! Fire! Fire!
All re - turn - ing from the burn-ing Fire! Fire! Fire!

Marching 'Round the Schoolroom

Rote Song

ANN UNDERHILL

W. OTTO MIESSNER

March-ing, march-ing round a - bout the schoolroom;
March-ing, march-ing round a - bout the schoolroom;

Heads e -rect, eyes a-head, like the sol-diers on pa -rade.
Up we file, on we file, past the window, down the aisle;

March - ing, march - ing, do not fall be - hind!
March - ing, march - ing, by the o - pen door;

Keep in step as " we turn and wind.
Now we stand at our desks once more!

Cradle Song

Observation Song

ELIZABETH PRENTISS

GERMAN FOLK SONG

Sleep, ba - by, sleep!

Thy fa - ther guards the sheep,

Thy moth - er shakes the dream-land tree,

And down fall pleas - ant dreams for thee.

Sleep, ba - by, sleep!

The Organ Man

Reading Song

Abbie Farwell Brown

ADAPTED

The old I-tal-ian or-gan man—
The lit-tle chil-dren like his tunes,

He trav-els all the day,
And dance a-bout the street.

He sells his mu-sic when he can,
I hope the hun-gry or-gan man

But man-y turn a-way.
Has all he wants to eat.

67

Toyland

Rote Song

EUGENE FIELD

W. OTTO MIESSNER

Oh, how do you get to Toy - land,
And oh, but it's gay in Toy - land,

Of all lit - tle ones the joy - land?
This bright, mer - ry girl and boy - land!

Just fol - low your nose, And go on tip - toes;
The wool - ly dogs white That nev - er will bite,

It's on - ly a min - ute to Toy-land, To Toy - land.
You'll meet on the high-way to Toy-land, To Toy - land.

Rowing Song

Rote Song

Ann Underhill

W. Otto Miessner

Our oars in the row-locks are creak-ing a song;
We bend to our oars and we sing as we row;

They push back the wa-ter and send us a-long.
It rains and the wind is be-gin-ning to blow.

Our jack-ets are thin; We're wet to the skin;
White foam rip-ples past; We're an-chored at last!

But keep up your cour-age we're stur-dy and strong!
And back to our homes now we hap-pi-ly go!

The Happy Eskimo

Rote Song

FREDERICK MANLEY

ELEANOR SMITH

Lightly

1. The hap - py lit - tle Es - ki - mo,—
2. My sled is i - dle in the hall;
3. Jack Frost is with him all the year,

He rides up - on a sled;
The ground is bare of snow;
And makes him lots of snow;

His dogs out - strip the winds that blow
The night comes ear - ly in the fall,
And i - cy hill - sides smooth and clear

A-cross the gleam-ing ice and snow,
And when I hear my moth-er call,
To coast and slide on with-out fear—

Be-neath the north-ern lights that show
I have to say good night to all,
O how I wish Jack Frost were here,

Like sil - ver o - ver - head.
And to my bed-room go.
And I an Es - ki - mo!

The Elephant

Observation Song

ELEANOR SMITH

The el - e - phant's a trav - el - er
And so he takes a room - y trunk

From far a - cross the seas;
Wher - ev - er he may be

He trav - els round with cir - cus - es
To hold the man - y gifts he gets

And big men - ag - er - ies.
For fun - ny tricks we see.

May

Reading Song

ABBIE FARWELL BROWN   ADAPTED

Sweet   May   puts   on   a   crown
Fair   Spring - time   al - ways   brings

Of   rich   and   gold - en   down;
Sweet   breath   of   grow - ing   things,

A   rus - tling   robe   of   silk - en   green,
And   all   the   love - ly   swarms that   fly

A   blos - som   cov - ered   gown.
On   shin - ing,   gauz - y   wings.

Rain Song

Rote Song

ELEANOR SMITH · ELEANOR SMITH

Allegretto

Rain, rain, do not go, Rain, rain, we love you so!
Rain, rain, do not go, Rain, rain, we love you so!

Make us mu - sic on the pane,
Make the brook-let's wa - ter high,

Drum to wild wind's fid - dle-strain,
Then our tall boots we may try;

Make us pools where - in to float
Wash the grim - y cit - y clean,

Ev - 'ry lit - tle paint - ed boat.
Make the lawns and mead-ows green.

The Owl

Rote Song

REBECCA B. FORESMAN

ETHELBERT NEVIN

Moderato

O round - faced owl, you look so wise,
I won - der where you got your name

With that large head and those big eyes;
For wis - dom, tell me whence it came;

But still, I'm sure, you nev - er do
He looked at me as if he knew,

A thing but say "To - whit, to - whoo."
But sim - ply said "To - whit, to - whoo."

The Echo Man

Rote Song

SARAH GRAMES CLARK   ADOLF WEIDIG

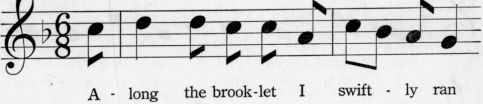

A - long   the brook-let   I   swift - ly ran

To   call   a - cross   to   the   Ech - o Man,

And   he,   po - lite - ly   as   can   be,

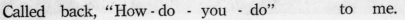

Called back, "How - do - you - do"   to   me.

A Dew Drop

Rote Song

Frank Dempster Sherman
By permission of Houghton Mifflin Company

W. W. Gilchrist

Lit - tle drop of dew
When the day is bright

Like a gem you are;
On the grass you lie;

I be - lieve that you
Tell me, then, at night

Must have been a star.
Are you in the sky?

Swing Song
Rote Song

L. C. LOCKLEY

WILLIAM J. KRAFT

Swing low, Swing high,

Up in the air we fly;

O - ver the tree-tops we swing,

Racing the birds on the wing;

Swing low, Swing high,

Up in the air we fly.

The Airplane

Rote Song

Ann Underhill · Anna Bergstrom

Lis - ten to the hum - ming sound,

Br - r - r - r;

Near - er, near - er, turn - ing round,

Br - r - r - r;

Like a bird in the sky,

See the air - plane whiz - zing by! Br - r - r - r.

Evening Prayer

Reading Song

ELEANOR SMITH

Now the world is sleep - ing, Lit - tle stars are peep - ing;

Fa - ther, in Thy keep - ing May the chil - dren rest.

The Lace Seller

Study Song

ANN UNDERHILL

OLD SONG

Come and buy my laces, dear, Peep in - to my bas - ket,
In and out my nee - dle flies, With the thread it tra - ces

See this love - ly col - lar here, Yours if you but ask it.
Pat - terns fine before your eyes; Come and buy my lac - es.

Evening Star
Reading Song

ABBIE FARWELL BROWN

F. A. L. JACOB

Sun-set glow is fad-ing In the west-ern sky,
Now the star of eve-ning Shin-ing clear and bright,

Birds have stopped their singing, Cool winds rus - tle by.
With its stead - y gleam - ing Wel-comes in the night.

Morning Song
Study Song

ANN UNDERHILL

CARL WILHELM

Wake, lit - tle chil - dren, Sing and be gay!

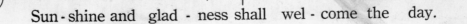

Sun - shine and glad - ness shall wel - come the day.

Sleep, Dolly, Sleep

Rote Song

RUTH STEPHENS PORTER

RUTH STEPHENS PORTER

Sleep, dol - ly, sleep,

Don't let lit - tle eye - lids peep.

I am pre-par-ing a glad sur-prise
I am mak-ing a dress of blue

For   you,   my own, when you   o - pen your eyes;
To   cov - er my darl - ing, it's   all___ for you;

Sleep,   dol - ly,   sleep,___

Don't let lit - tle eye - lids peep.

Knitting Song

Rote Song

Agnes Choate Wonson

W. Otto Miessner

My Grand - ma sits and swift - ly knits;

Her nee - dles click, they move so quick,

And while they glis - ten to and fro,

She tells me tales of long a - go, How, as a lit - tle girl,

She'd sit be - side her Grand-ma-ma and knit!_____

Marbles
Reading Song

ANN UNDERHILL

ELEANOR SMITH

Come and play at mar - bles!
Swift - er than an ar - row

See my hand - some beau - ties.
Leap - ing from your fin - gers,

Here's a qui - et place to stay;
Ah! You've hit it square and true!

You may be the first to play.
Now I'll see what I can do.

Dancing Lesson

Study Song

Ann Underhill

Osbourne McConathy

Left foot for - ward!
Left foot, for - ward!

Give the oth - er foot next a chance;
First go backward and then ad - vance;

Right foot for - ward!
Right foot, for - ward!

Soon you'll learn how to dance._____
Now you're learn - ing to dance._____

Chanticleer

Rote Song

KATHERINE TYNAN

G. A. GRANT-SCHAEFER

Of all the birds from East to West

That tune - ful are and dear,

I love that farm - yard bird the best,

They call him Chant - i - cleer.

Sunflowers

Rote Song

W. Otto Miéssner   W. Otto Miessner

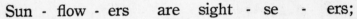

Sun - flow - ers   are   sight - se - ers;

They   grow   so   high   and   tall

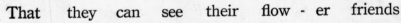

That   they   can   see   their   flow - er   friends

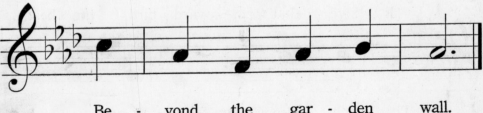

Be - yond   the   gar - den   wall.

Choose Your Partner

Rote Song

NANCY BYRD TURNER

SWEDISH SINGING GAME

Choose your part - ner and join the dance

As fast as you can take her,

Down through the cen - ter and back a - gain

Turn her and swing her, and give her then

The best bow you can make her!

Children's Hymn

Abbie Farwell Brown

Sicilian Melody

Lord, dis - miss__ us__ with thy bless - ing,

Send us on our__ hap - py way;

Let__ thy__ love, our hearts__ pos - ses-sing,

Guide__ our__ steps__ from__ day to day.

America

SAMUEL F. SMITH

HENRY CAREY

My country, 'tis of thee, Sweet land of lib - er - ty,

Of thee I sing; Land where my fa - thers died,

Land of the Pil - grims' pride, From ev - 'ry____

moun - tain side Let____ free - dom ring.

INDEX

34